Longman Study Texts

Equus

Longman Study Texts

General editor: Richard Adams

Titles in the series:

Animal Farm *George Orwell*
Brave New World *Aldous Huxley*
Great Expectations *Charles Dickens*
Pride and Prejudice *Jane Austen*
Wuthering Heights *Emily Brontë*
The Royal Hunt of the Sun *Peter Shaffer*
The Winslow Boy *Terence Rattigan*
Pygmalion *Bernard Shaw*
Saint Joan *Bernard Shaw*
The Importance of Being Earnest *Oscar Wilde*
Equus *Peter Shaffer*